Are You Too High?

A PRACTICAL GUIDE
NOT MEDICAL ADVICE

BRIAN BOX BROWN
NOT A DOCTOR

Written and illustrated by Brian Box Brown

Brian Box Brown is a New York Times best-selling comic artist and cannabis activist from Philadelphia. See more of his work at @boxbrown on Twitter and Instagram.

Special thanks to Jessilyn Dolan!

Edited by Esther Gabriel and Elizabeth Sly

Published by Neatoco LLC
ISBN: 978-1-956562-12-5
Printed in Canada

HERE IS A FUNNY STORY FROM 2006:

MICHIGAN COP EDWARD SANCHEZ SEIZES A QUARTER OZ. OF WEED.

HE AND HIS WIFE MADE WEED BROWNIES.

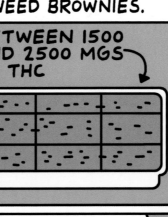

BETWEEN 1500 AND 2500 MGS OF THC

THEY ATE THEM ALL

DAMMN

LATER:

TIME IS MOVING SO SLOW RIGHT NOW

I THINK I'M DYING.

9-1-1

BEEP
BOOP
BEEP

SEND AN AMBULANCE.

WHAT'S THE SCORE OF THE REDWINGS GAME THERE?

I WANNA MAKE SURE I'M NOT IN A PARALLEL UNIVERSE.

HERE'S A SIMILAR FUNNY STORY FROM 2003*:

NJ RESIDENT BRIAN BROWN BUYS A QUARTER OZ. OF "DANK" WEED. 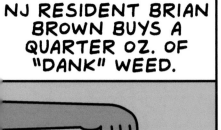	HE AND HIS FRIENDS HAD HAD A FEW BEERS. 	THEY MADE WEED BUTTER... 
...THEN BROWNIES. 	THEY HAD TO WAIT FOR THEM TO COOL. 	EACH BROWNIE WAS PROBABLY A LEGIT 250 MG OF THC, BUT THEY DIDN'T KNOW JACKSHIT ABOUT DOSING BACK THEN. 
HE BECAME GLUED TO A CHAIR.	COULDN'T MOVE, FELT THE PRESSURE OF GRAVITY WEIGHING HIM DOWN. 	PEOPLE WROTE ON HIS FACE. 

*IT'S NOT QUITE AS FUNNY TO ME PERSONALLY

WITH SOME DRUGS, OVERDOSE CAN BE SERIOUSLY BAD FOR YOUR HEALTH AND EVEN KILL YOU.

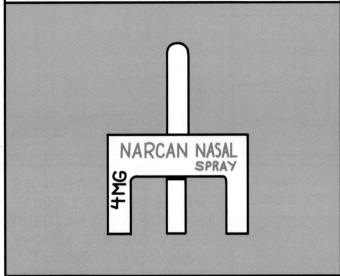

BUT WITH CANNABIS OVER CONSUMPTION, PEOPLE JUST *THINK* THEY'RE DYING.

THE COP IN THE 9-1-1 TAPE SAID HIMSELF:

BUT HE WAS NOT DYING. IN FACT, HE WAS PAYING ATTENTION TO A HOCKEY GAME.

YOU ARE GONNA WANT TO STOCK UP NOW ON EVERYTHING YOU MIGHT WANT. STUFF FOR NOW, STUFF FOR LATER AND STUFF FOR WAY LATER.
JUST UNASHAMEDLY PURCHASE SNACKS
TRUST ME HERE. OVERBUY.
NO SLIPPY
PUS

I'D GET:

MAYBE EVEN:

FUCK IT:

ARE YOU STILL FEELING TOO HIGH? IF YOU JUST SMOKED OR VAPED YOU'LL FEEL BETTER SOON.

IF YOU TOOK EDIBILES IT WILL BE A SLOWER PROCESS. BUT, I ASSURE YOU THAT YOU WILL CHILL OUT EVENTUALLY. PROMISE.

EDIBLES ARE TRICKY TO DOSE. EVEN FOR CERTIFIED PROFESSIONALS LIKE MYSELF, ACCIDENTAL OVERINGESTION HAPPENS.

NOOBS SHOULD REMEMBER: TAKING A PUFF IS PROBABLY THE SMALLEST DOSE YOU CAN TAKE. IT HAS THE QUICKEST ONSET AND WEARS OFF FASTEST.

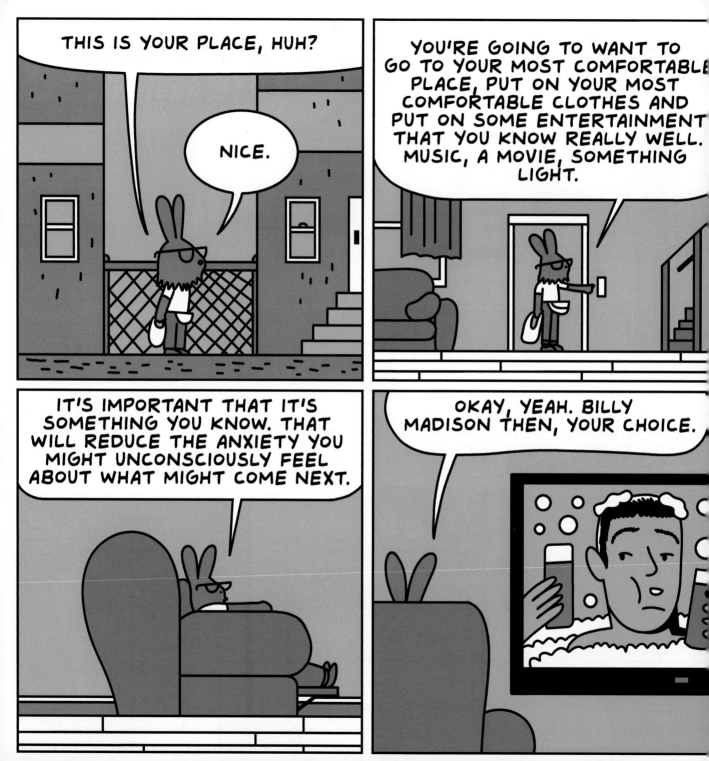

YOU SHOULD BE CONSIDERABLY MORE CHILL NOW. I KNOW I AM. BUT JUST IN CASE, I'M GOING TO TEXT MY FRIEND WHO IS A CANNABIS NURSE. THAT'S RIGHT, THEY HAVE CANNABIS NURSES NOW. NURSES HELP PEOPLE.
CHLOROPHYLL? MORE LIKE *BOROPHYLL!!*

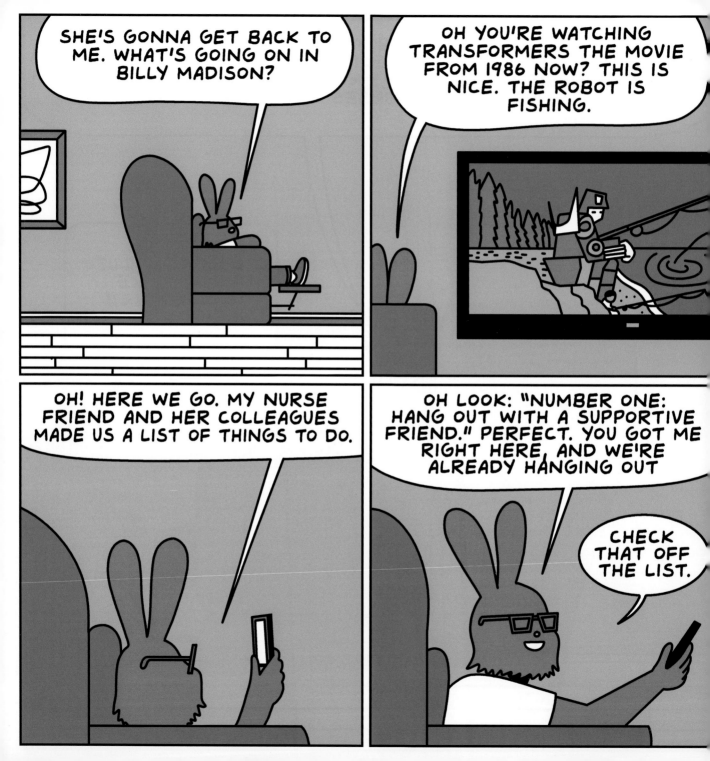

SO, IN YOUR BRAIN, YOU HAVE SOMETHING CALLED A CB RECEPTOR. IT RECEIVES CANNABINOIDS, LIKE THC, WHICH MAKES YOU FEEL HIGH.

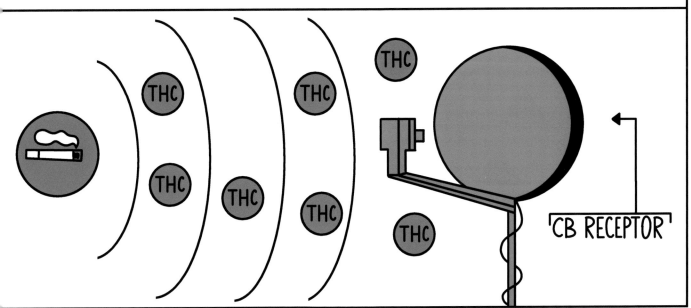

WHEN YOU CHEW PEPPERCORNS, IT RELEASES BETA CARYOPHYLLENE, WHICH WORKS LIKE A CANNABINOID. (IT'S IN A LOT OF CANNABIS STRAINS.)

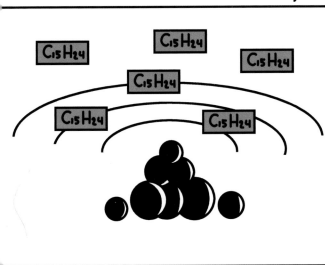

YOUR CB RECEPTOR RECEIVES BETA CARYOPHYLLENE, LIMITING ITS ABILITY TO RECEIVE THC.

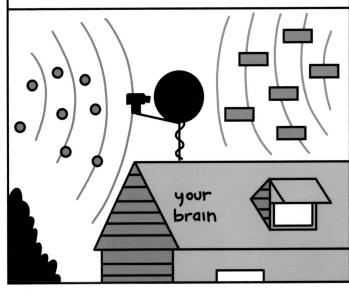

TAKING CBD WORKS SIMILARLY. IT ATTACHES TO YOUR CB RECEPTORS INSTEAD OF THC.

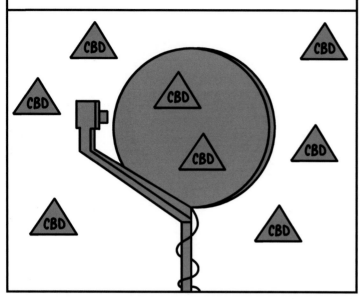

ONE NOTE: YOU SHOULD TRY TO TAKE PURE CBD AND NOT CBD HEMP FLOWER.

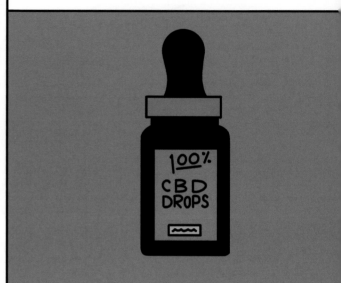

THIS IS BECAUSE HEMP CBD FLOWER HAS A LITTLE THC IN IT.

IF YOU'RE FEELING LIKE YOU TOOK TOO MUCH THC, YOU WOULDN'T WANT TO ADD MORE.

OTHER STUFF YOU CAN TAKE:

ORANGES, LEMON WATER

B-COMPLEX

NIACIN

PINE NUTS, PEANUT BUTTER

.gif
creamy P. butter

OLIVETOL, A THC INHIBITOR

OLIVETOL
25mg

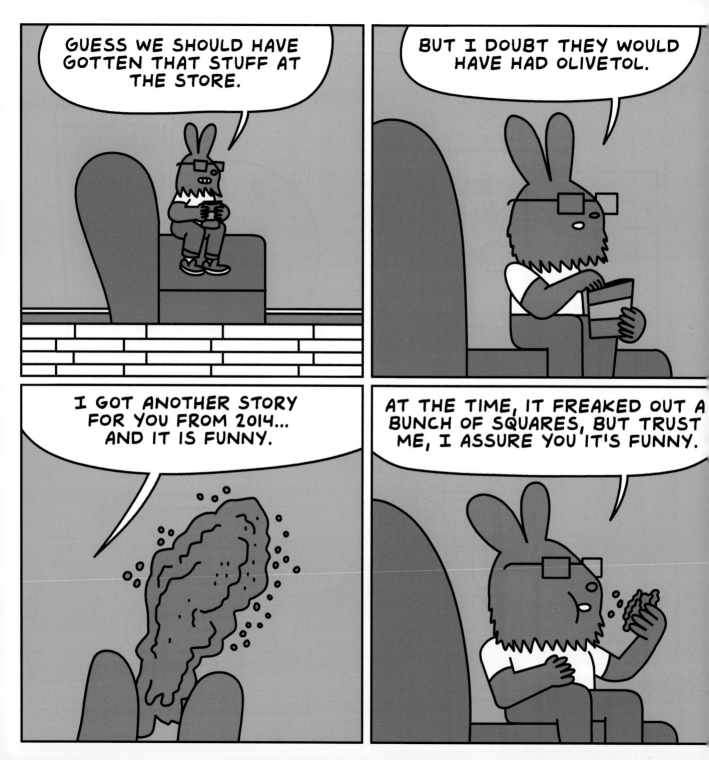

WAY BACK IN 2014, COLORADO HAD JUST LEGALIZED WEED AND NEW YORK TIMES WRITER MAUREEN DOUD HAPPENED TO BE IN DENVER.
NO PARKING
TO GO
APT 4 RENT
NEED GUITAR PLAYER
SHOULD I? WHY NOT?
SHOW I.D.

MAUREEN BOUGHT A THC CANDY BAR AND DID NOT NOTE ITS STRENGTH.

THEN SHE TOOK A BITE. THESE ARE SEPARATED INTO DOSES, BUT SHE TOOK A BITE.

SHE WAITED AN UNDISCLOSED AMOUNT OF TIME AND DIDN'T FEEL ANYTHING.

THESE EDIBLES AIN'T SHIT.

SO SHE TOOK ANOTHER BITE.

WITHOUT KNOWING HOW MANY MILIGRAMS OF THC SHE CONSUMED, IT'S HARD TO KNOW HOW MUCH SHE HAD OVERDID IT.

I'M NOT EXACTLY SURE WHAT SHE WAS EXPECTING TO HAPPEN.

SHE WOKE UP THE NEXT DAY AND FELT FINE ENOUGH TO GO INTERVIEW A PURVEYOR OF CANNABIS EDIBLES.

WHY SHOULD THE INDUSTRY SUFFER BECAUSE 5% OF THE POPULATION HAS PROBLEMS WITH DOSING?

YOU SOUND A LITTLE PARANOID.

SHE REALLY ENDED THE PIECE LIKE THAT.

DOSING! IT'S SO IMPORTANT.

BUT THIS ISN'T CONSIDERED BUDWEISER'S FAULT.

OR JIM BEAM'S FAULT OR WHATEVER Y'ALL ARE SIPPING ON THESE DAYS'S FAULT.

PEOPLE ARE EXPECTED TO KNOW THEIR LIMITS AND Y'KNOW, HANDLE THEIR SHIT.

IF YOU'RE INEXPERIENCED WITH CANNABIS DOSING, TO BE SAFE, YOU NEED TO SLOWLY FIGURE OUT WHAT'S THE RIGHT DOSE FOR YOU.

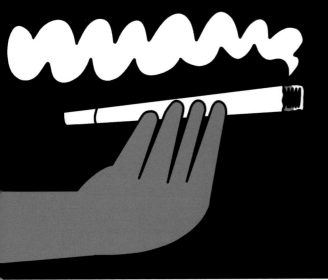

IDEALLY, A LOW TOLERANCE NOOB SHOULD TAKE A PUFF OFF THIS JOINT.

THEN WAIT A FEW MINUTES.

ASSESS HOW THEY FEEL AND REPEAT AS NECESSARY.

AM I HIGH YET?

THIS ALLOWS THE USER TO SLOWLY APPROACH THEIR HIGH AND STOP BEFORE OVERDOING IT.

IF YOU TAKE AN EDIBLE, YOU MUST PAY ATTENTION TO THE LABEL. IN THE LEGAL MARKET PRODUCTS *SHOULD* BE PROPERLY LABELED.

100MG THC PER BAR, 10MG PER PIECE

IF YOU'RE A REGULAR SMOKER, YOU MIGHT WANNA TAKE 10 MG YOUR FIRST TIME. IT'S WORTHWHILE TO START SMALL; YOU CAN ALWAYS TAKE MORE.

REMEMBER ALSO: YOUR EXPERIENCE WILL BE AFFECTED BY YOUR SIZE AND METABOLIC RATE. SOME PEOPLE EVEN HAVE NATURALLY HIGHER OR LOWER TOLERANCES.

CHEERS!

IF YOU'RE TAKING A HOMEMADE PRODUCT, YOU CAN CALCULATE HOW MUCH THC IS IN EACH PIECE.

I MADE THEM WITH HALF AN OUNCE.

ONE GRAM OF 20% THC WEED EQUALS 200 MG OF THC. 14 GRAMS OF 20% THC WEED EQUALS 2800 MG.

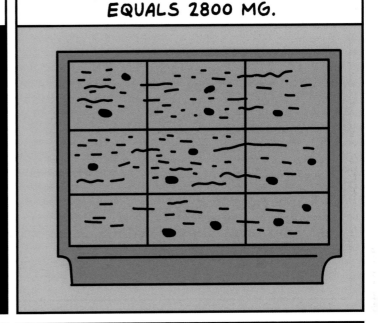

2800 MG DIVIDED BY 9 BROWNIES...

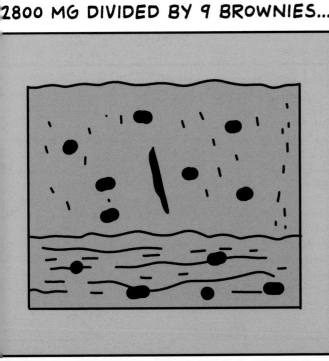

...311 MG PER BROWNIE! DIVIDE THAT THING UP! SHARE IT WITH MORE PALS! SAVE SOME FOR LATER!

THERE ARE ALSO ILLICIT MARKET EDIBLES LIKE THIS WHICH CAN OFTEN BE MISLABLED.

THESE ARE MOSTLY REGULAR SNACKS BOUGHT AT A STORE BUT COVERED IN THC DISTILLATE

IT'S BEEN MY EXPERIENCE THAT THEY'RE NOT OFTEN EVENLY DOSED PER PIECE NOR CORRECTLY LABELED ON THE PACKAGE.

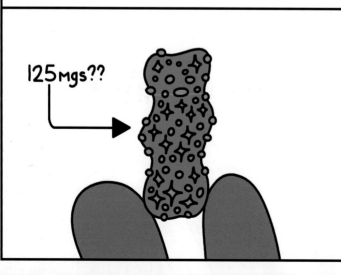

125mgs??

THESE ARE ALMOST ENTIRELY UNPREDICTABLE AND TASTE WEIRD.

WHAT FLAVOR WAS THAT??

green.

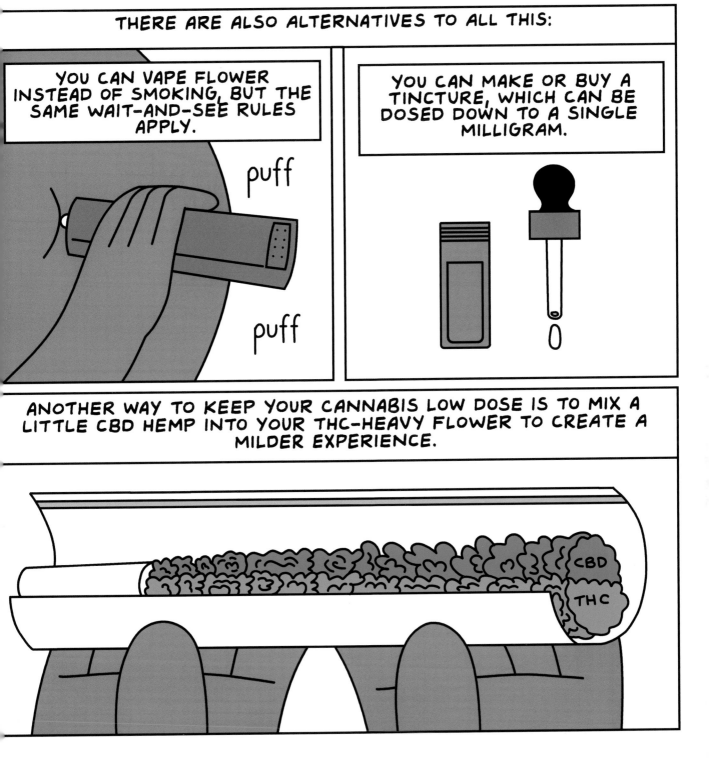

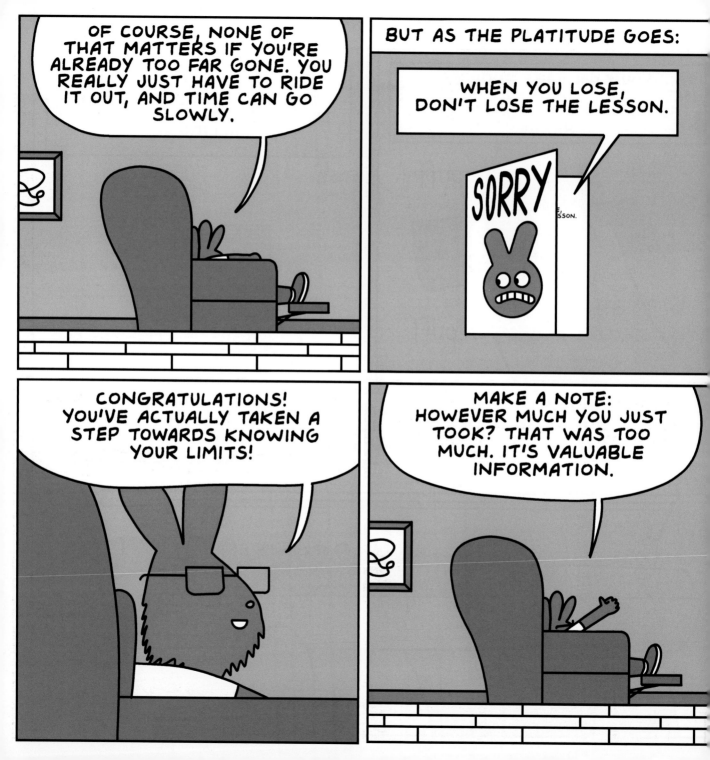

HINDSIGHT IS 20/20, BUT THAT COP SHOULD HAVE JUST ORDERED A PIZZA INSTEAD OF CALLING 9-1-1.

AT THE HOSPITAL, THEY PROBABLY HAD HIM JUST SIT AND WAIT AND DRINK WATER AND EAT HOSPITAL FOOD. ALSO, AT THE TIME, IF HE WASN'T A COP, HE MAY HAVE FACED CRIMINAL CHARGES.

AND 9-1-1 CALLS ARE A MATTER OF PUBLIC RECORD.

FOOD ORDERS ARE NOT (THANKFULLY).

ONE MORE THING: ONE OF THE EFFECTS OF CANNABIS IS THAT YOU THINK THINGS.

AND SOMETIMES YOU THINK THINGS YOU DON'T LIKE.

BUT THEY'RE JUST THOUGHTS. YOU CAN TAKE THEM OR LEAVE THEM.

IF YOUR THOUGHTS ARE BUGGING YOU OUT, YOU CAN LEAVE THEM. EVEN IF JUST UNTIL LATER, WHEN YOU'VE SOBERED UP.

WANT TO KNOW WHAT TO DO IF THIS HAPPENS AND YOU'RE UNABLE TO GO HOME AND WATCH SOME CARTOONS OR ANIME OR WHATEVER?

TRY TO DO A TINY VERSION OF THAT.

EVEN IF YOU'RE JUST GOING THERE IN YOUR MIND'S EYE.

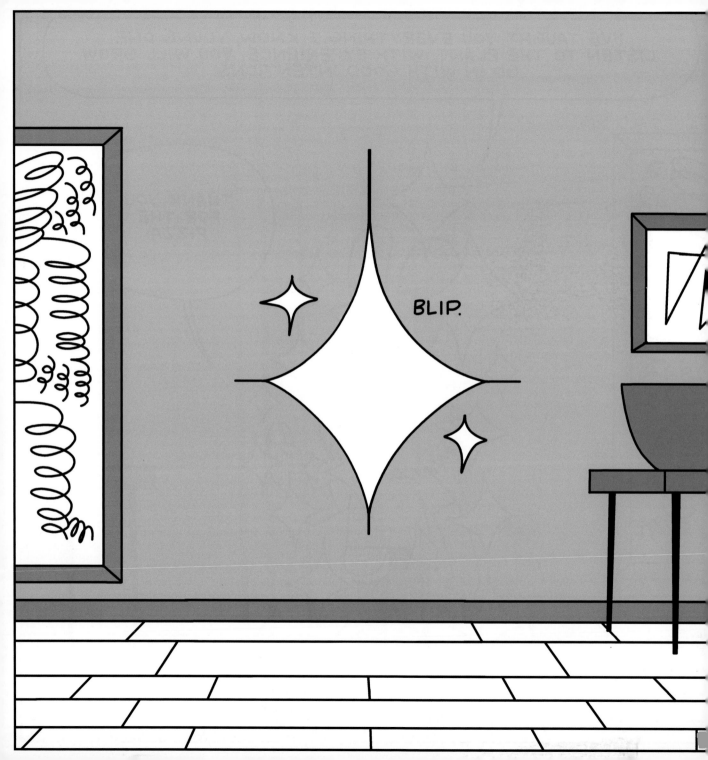